The Twelve Days of *Hula*

A Counting Book from Hawai'i

written by
Beth Greenway

❀

illustrated by
Kristi Petosa-Sigel

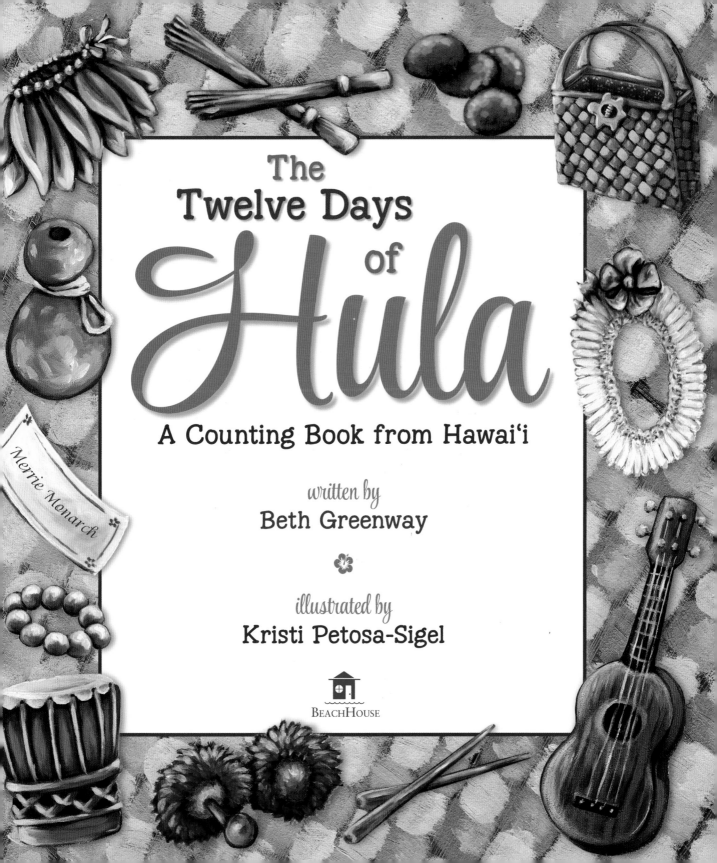

BEACHHOUSE

ISBN-10: 1-933067-56-X· ISBN-13: 978-1-933067-56-8
Library of Congress Control Number: 2013942048

Design by Jane Gillespie
First Printing, October 2013

BeachHouse Publishing, LLC
PO Box 5464 · Kāne‘ohe, Hawai‘i 96744
email: info@beachhousepublishing.com
www.beachhousepublishing.com

Printed in China

Visit our website to learn about
our children's book iPhone™ apps,
which can be purchased at iTunes™ now!

For Aunty Joanie and Aunty Lili
—Beth Greenway

To my students at Lanikai Elementary School
with whom I have shared my passion for art the past ten
years. You are my constant inspiration!
—Kristi Petosa-Sigel

1

On the first day of hula
my kumu gave to me
a hula bag
from a hala tree.

hula bag—used to hold hula implements;
some woven from lauhala, the leaves
of the hala tree

2

On the second day of hula
my kumu gave to me
two ʻulīʻulī
and a hula bag
from a hala tree.

ʻulīʻulī—a gourd rattle filled with seeds

3

On the third day of hula
my kumu gave to me
three ti leaf skirts,
two ‘ulī‘ulī,
and a hula bag
from a hala tree.

4

On the fourth day of hula
my kumu gave to me
four kūpeʻe,
three ti leaf skirts,
two ʻulīʻulī,
and a hula bag
from a hala tree.

kūpeʻe—bracelet or anklet often made
from natural materials

5

On the fifth day of hula
my kumu gave to me
five Kamaka ʻukulele,
four kūpeʻe,
three ti leaf skirts,
two ʻulīʻulī,
and a hula bag
from a hala tree.

6

On the sixth day of hula
my kumu gave to me
six pūʻili,
five Kamaka ʻukulele,
four kūpeʻe,
three ti leaf skirts,
two ʻulīʻulī,
and a hula bag
from a hala tree.

pūʻili—split bamboo stick used alone
or in pairs to provide rhythm

7

On the seventh day of hula
my kumu gave to me
seven sharkskin drums,
six pūʻili,
five Kamaka ʻukulele,
four kūpeʻe,
three ti leaf skirts,
two ʻulīʻulī,
and a hula bag
from a hala tree.

8

On the eighth day of hula
my kumu gave to me
eight kālaʻau,
seven sharkskin drums,
six pūʻili
five Kamaka ʻukulele,
four kūpeʻe,
three ti leaf skirts,
two ʻulīʻulī,
and a hula bag
from a hala tree.

kālaʻau—two wooden sticks
that you hit together rhythmically

9

On the ninth day of hula
my kumu gave to me
nine ipu heke,
eight kālaʻau,
seven sharkskin drums,
six pūʻili,
five Kamaka ʻukulele,
four kūpeʻe,
three ti leaf skirts,
two ʻulīʻulī,
and a hula bag
from a hala tree.

ipu heke—double gourd drum

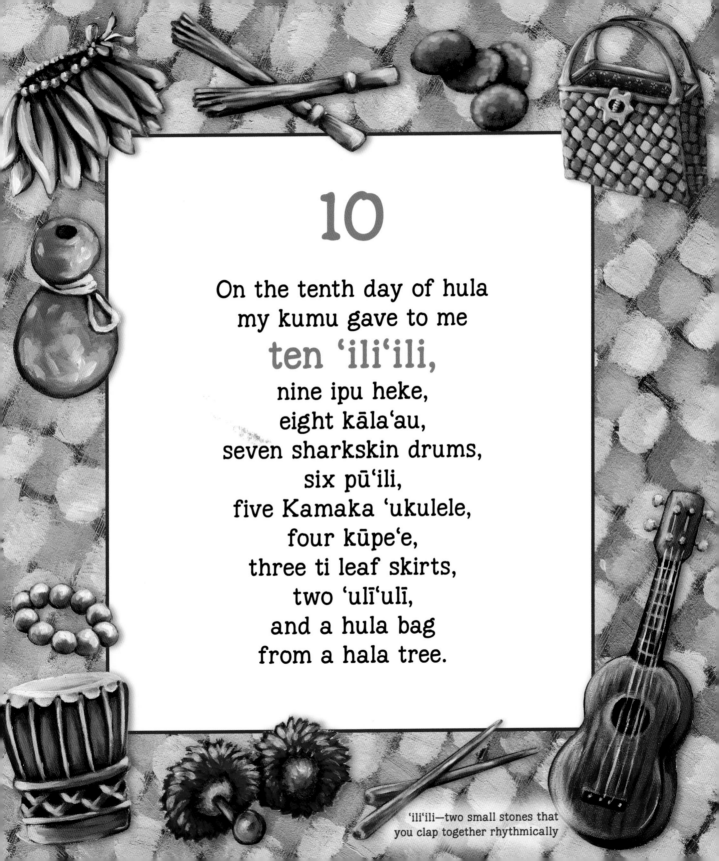

10

On the tenth day of hula
my kumu gave to me
ten ʻiliʻili,
nine ipu heke,
eight kālaʻau,
seven sharkskin drums,
six pūʻili,
five Kamaka ʻukulele,
four kūpeʻe,
three ti leaf skirts,
two ʻulīʻulī,
and a hula bag
from a hala tree.

ʻiliʻili—two small stones that
you clap together rhythmically

11

On the eleventh day of hula
my kumu gave to me
eleven ginger lei,
ten ʻiliʻili,
nine ipu heke,
eight kālaʻau,
seven sharkskin drums,
six pūʻili,
five Kamaka ʻukulele,
four kūpeʻe,
three ti leaf skirts,
two ʻulīʻulī,
and a hula bag
from a hala tree.

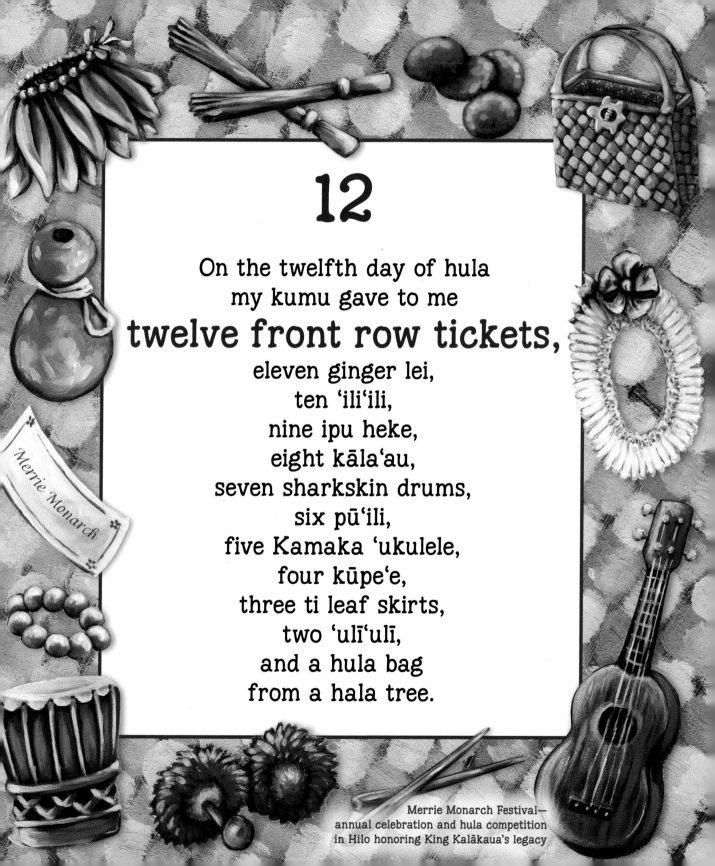

12

On the twelfth day of hula
my kumu gave to me
twelve front row tickets,
eleven ginger lei,
ten ʻiliʻili,
nine ipu heke,
eight kālaʻau,
seven sharkskin drums,
six pūʻili,
five Kamaka ʻukulele,
four kūpeʻe,
three ti leaf skirts,
two ʻulīʻulī,
and a hula bag
from a hala tree.

Merrie Monarch Festival—
annual celebration and hula competition
in Hilo honoring King Kalākaua's legacy

About the Author

Beth Greenway and her family lived on Oʻahu. After raising three hula dancers, she and her husband retired to Virginia. Her previous books include: *A Lei for Everyday*, *Waikiki Lullaby*, and *Hawaiʻi's Food Trucks on the Go*. She has also been featured in *Highlights* Magazine for Children.

❁ ❁ ❁

About the Illustrator

Kristi Petosa-Sigel was born and raised on a small island in the Pacific Northwest where she would draw and paint as a child. She found the quiet beach community of Kailua at the age of twenty-one and has made it her home with her husband and their three artistic children. In addition to teaching art at Lanikai Elementary School, Kristi has realized her childhood dream and has illustrated numerous children's books, including *Magic Moon Dreams*, *A Butterfly Tale*, *Let's Find Koa*, and *Hōkū the Stargazer*.